Presented to

Michael

Isaac

BARNES

METHODIST CHURCH

Christian Art, Exeter, 01392 77277

My First Bible
in Story and Song

Published by Brimax Books Ltd, Newmarket, England
Reprinted 1994.
Printed in France by Pollina, 85400 Luçon - n° 63834

My First Bible
in Story and Song

Illustrated by Diana Bowles

Brimax • Newmarket • England

God made everything that we can see.
He made the sky, the moon and the stars.

God made the fish that swim in the sea.

God made the animals, both big and small.

God made each little bird and every
tiny flower. He made both the sun and
the rain, helping everything to grow.

God made all the little children
and mothers and fathers too.

All things bright and beautiful
All creatures great and small,
All things wise and wonderful
The Lord God made them all.

A long time ago there lived a
man called Noah. God told
Noah that it would rain for
days and days and all the land
would be covered with water.

God told Noah to make an ark
and take his family and two of
every kind of animal into the ark
so that they would all be safe.

The animals went in two by two
Hurrah! Hurrah!
The animals went in two by two
Hurrah! Hurrah!

The animals went in two by two,
The elephant and the kangaroo.
They all went into the ark
So they could get out of the rain.

Soon the storm came and it rained. All the land was covered with water, but the ark could float. Noah, his family and all the animals were safe.

When the storm had gone away
and the sun was shining again,
Noah said thank you to God and
all the animals left the ark.

God asked Moses to go to Egypt and
lead His people to a new land where
they would all be happy. Thousands
of people followed Moses.

When the King of Egypt found out
that there was no one to do all the
work, he sent his soldiers to bring
all the people back again.

When the people saw the soldiers coming after them they were afraid. Moses said, "Do not be afraid. God will save us."

God opened up a path through the sea
and Moses led the people to safety.

The new land was far away, but
God helped His people. God made
bread rain from Heaven when they
were hungry.

Moses told the people that God
would always look after them.
They must pray to God and teach
their children to love God and
love one another.

Daniel was a man who loved God
and prayed every day. Some men
did not believe in God. They said
that everyone must pray to the king.

Daniel did not listen to these men.
The men were angry and they put
Daniel in the lions' den. The lions
were hungry but Daniel was not
afraid.

Daniel knew the lions would not eat him. He knew God would save him. God closed the mouths of the lions so they could not eat Daniel.

There once was a man named Jonah.
God wanted Jonah to help Him. Jonah
did not want to so he ran away to sea.

Soon there was a big storm. Jonah knew it was because God was angry with him. Jonah told the sailors to throw him into the sea so that they would not die.

They threw Jonah into the water.
A big whale swallowed up Jonah.
Jonah was now in the tummy of the
whale. He did not know what to do.

Jonah was very sorry that he did not listen to God. Jonah prayed to God to help him. God listened to Jonah and saved him. Jonah then obeyed God.

Near a little town called Bethlehem,
Mary and Joseph needed a place to
stay. There was no room for them
anywhere. They had to sleep in a
stable with the animals.

Baby Jesus was born in the night.
There was nowhere for the baby
to sleep, so Joseph put some soft
straw in a manger and made a
little bed for the Baby Jesus.

In the fields some shepherds looking after their sheep saw a white light in the sky. An angel told them, "Go to Bethlehem. Jesus is born."

The shepherds went to the stable.
They knelt beside the Baby Jesus.
They knew he was very special.

Wise men from far away followed
a bright star in the sky. It led them
to the stable. They gave presents
to Baby Jesus.

Away in a manger
No crib for a bed,
The little Lord Jesus
Lay down his sweet head.

The stars in the bright sky
Look down where he lay,
The little Lord Jesus
Asleep in the hay.

Jesus grew up in a little town called Nazareth. He helped his mother to carry water.

Jesus liked to help Joseph too.
At the end of the day he helped
Joseph put away his tools.

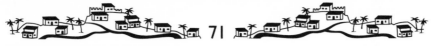

When Jesus grew up he knew that he had God's work to do. He told the people about God. He told them that God loves everyone.

Jesus cared about the sick people.
He could do things an ordinary
person could not do. He made a
blind man see again.

He made a crippled man walk again.

Jesus told many stories.
One day a man was attacked by
robbers. They took his donkey and
all his money. They left him by the
side of the road, hurt and bleeding.

After a little while a man passed by.
He saw that the man was hurt,
but he did not help him.

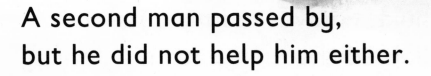

A second man passed by,
but he did not help him either.

Then a third man came along the road. He saw that the man was hurt. He washed his cuts and helped the man onto his donkey.

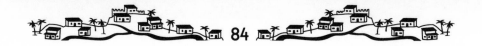

He took the man to an inn and
gave the inn-keeper money to
look after him.

Jesus said, "Always help those
who cannot help themselves,
as the third man did."

One day when the people were
hungry Jesus asked if anyone had
any food. A little boy had five
loaves and two fish.

There were thousands of hungry people. Five loaves and two fish could not feed them all.

But Jesus held up the food and said thank you to God for it. Everyone was given food to eat.

No one knew how five loaves and
two fish could feed so many people.

Mothers brought their children to Jesus
so that he could bless them. Jesus told
stories to the children. Every little girl
and boy is special to Jesus.

Jesus loves the little children
All the children of the world,
Red, yellow black and white
All are precious in his sight,
Jesus loves the little children of the world.

Jesus said to remember him always.
He lives in Heaven and watches over
us every day. He listens to our prayers.

We are your little children,
To you dear God we pray,
Keep us safe through every day
In all we do, both work and play.

Help us when we cross the street
To think of others — take their hands.
Help us get to know and love
Those who come from other lands.